Thank you ...

... for buying this copy of

Andrew Brodie's **Best Handwriting for ages 4 – 7**.

The sheets can be photocopied onto paper, card or overhead projector transparencies. Please note that copies can only be made for use by the purchasing institution. Supplying copies to other schools, institutions or individuals breaches the copyright licence. Thank you for your help in this.

Andrew Brodie's **Best Handwriting for ages 4 – 7** includes:

... a complete handwriting policy for your school

... the correct way to hold the pen and the paper or book

... sitting comfortably and appropriately for writing

... the structure of individual letters

... correct techniques for joining letters

... capital letters and lower case letters

... punctuation marks and their use

... numerals and the pound sign

... a complete programme of work to encourage

neat, legible handwriting.

Many more activities can be found in our
three write-in Practice Books :   Best Handwriting Reception
                                        Best Handwriting Year 1
                                        Best Handwriting Year 2

To find details of our other publications, please visit our website:

www.acblack.com

Establishing Good Handwriting

Developing a Programme of Work

To establish good handwriting habits we recommend daily practice for approximately ten to fifteen minutes for just a few weeks. The good habits introduced should then be maintained throughout the school year, by providing children with reminders of what they have already learnt.

Pupils make best progress with handwriting when they are shown exactly how to form the letters. We suggest that the teacher demonstrates the letter structure on a whiteboard or blackboard or by photocopying our Practice Sheets on to Overhead Projector Transparencies and drawing the letter shapes on them. Each short handwriting lesson should start with this brief demonstration of the letters and words to be covered within the session. The children should then work on the photocopied sheets independently, with the teacher circulating to check letter formation and to offer praise and support. It is important that the children follow exactly the letter formation shown on the sheets. It is useful to make further practice in our Write-in Practice Books and in exercise books with lines to guide the writing. Some younger children may find it helpful to practise on plain paper rather than lines.

'Best Handwriting' includes a proposed School Handwriting Policy. Lower case letters, with joining ticks where appropriate, are introduced in Reception and Year 1. Simple joins are introduced in Year 2 and extended in Year 3. At Year 4 we introduce the more difficult letter joins to enable pupils to use a totally joined style of writing. This is practised and extended in Years 5 and 6.

Many children really enjoy handwriting practice. They gain particular satisfaction in seeing their own writing transformed over a short period of time.

Contents

Handwriting at Reception Level

Establishing good writing habits at Reception level is extremely important.

We will ensure that each child holds the pencil comfortably and appropriately:

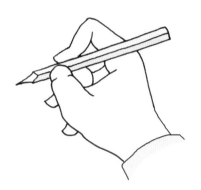

The pencil should be held between the thumb and first finger and should rest on the middle finger. It should be held at about 2 to 3 centimetres from the point.

We will provide 'chubby' pencils where appropriate. We will provide special pencil grips for those children who need them. We will consider the special requirements of left-handed children, ensuring that they hold their paper at an appropriate angle.

We will provide plenty of practice in using pencils, crayons and other writing implements to encourage children to gain confidence in drawing and in producing controlled lines.

We will encourage children to write each letter using controlled movements as shown in the letter formation guides below. Where appropriate with certain letters, we will introduce a 'tail' to encourage a style which will be easy to join in the future. We will check each child's writing as they work and record their progress on a class record sheet, indicating whether they can form each letter of the alphabet correctly.

a b c d e f g h i

j k l m n o p q

r s t u v w x y z

1 2 3 4 5 6 7 8 9 0

School Handwriting Policy

Handwriting at Year 1

We will further encourage the good handwriting habits developed in Reception.

We will ensure that each child holds the pencil comfortably and appropriately:

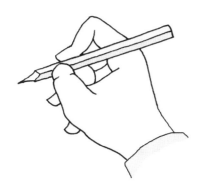

The pencil should be held between the thumb and first finger and should rest on the middle finger. It should be held at about 2 to 3 centimetres from the point.

We will provide 'chubby' pencils where appropriate. We will provide special pencil grips for those children who need them. We will consider the special requirements of left-handed children, ensuring that they hold their paper at an appropriate angle.

We will encourage children to write each letter as shown in the letter formation guides below. Where appropriate with certain letters, we will introduce a 'tail' so that the children will become accustomed to a style which will be easy to join in the future.

We will check each child's writing as they work and record their progress on a class record sheet, indicating with a tick whether they can form each letter of the alphabet correctly.

We will practise handwriting with the children alongside their spelling practice. We will encourage the use of tidy and well-formed writing in all independent work.

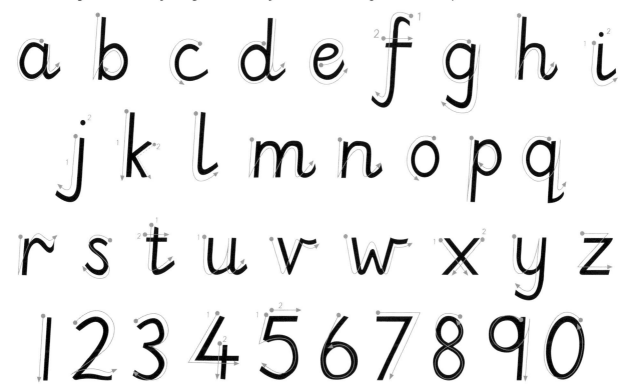

Handwriting at Year 2

We will continue to develop the handwriting patterns developed in Year 1.

We will ensure that each child holds the pencil comfortably and appropriately:

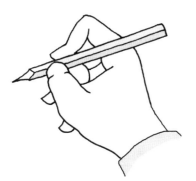

The pencil should be held between the thumb and first finger and should rest on the middle finger.
It should be held at about 2 to 3 centimetres from the point.

We will provide special pencil grips for those children who need them. We will consider the special requirements of left-handed children, ensuring that they hold their paper at an appropriate angle.

We will encourage children to write each letter using controlled movements as shown in the letter formation guides for Year 1.

We will introduce the four basic joins:

...slope joins to letters without ascenders:

an en in do um

...bridge joins to letters without ascenders:

on ri vo wa fi

...slope joins to letters with ascenders:

al eb it mb uh

...bridge joins to letters with ascenders:

oh wh rl ot

We will check each child's writing as they work and record their progress on a class record sheet, indicating with a tick whether they can form each type of join correctly.

We will practise handwriting with the children alongside their spelling and phonic practice and we will encourage the use of tidy writing in all independent work.

Handwriting at Year 2 continued

At this stage we will not join from the following letters:

bgjkpqsxyz

six   bags   jelly

foxes   keys

pin   quiz   zoo

1 2 3 4 5 6 7 8 9 0

Handwriting at Year 3

We will ensure that each child holds the pencil comfortably and appropriately:

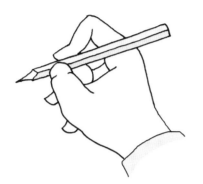

The pencil should be held between the thumb and first finger and should rest on the middle finger.
It should be held at about 2 to 3 centimetres from the point.

We will provide special pencil grips for those children who need them. We will consider the special requirements of left-handed children, ensuring that they hold their paper at an appropriate angle.

We will continue to develop the joins introduced in Year 2:

...slope joins to letters without ascenders: an en in do um

...bridge joins to letters without ascenders: on ri vo wa fi

...slope joins to letters with ascenders: al eb it mb uh

...bridge joins to letters with ascenders: oh wh rl ot

At this stage we will not join from the following letters: b g j p q s x y z

We will introduce the letter k as a joining letter, as shown here:

k kettle

We will check each child's writing as they work and record their progress on a class record sheet, indicating with a tick whether they can form each type of join correctly.

We will use 8mm lined paper, encouraging children to write letters of consistent size, where most letters sit on the line and descenders pass through it. We will show how to leave an appropriate gap between words, of approximately the width of two letters.

We will practise handwriting with the children alongside their spelling and phonic practice and we will encourage the use of tidy writing in all independent work, while at the same time developing speed and fluency. We will introduce the correct formations of question marks, exclamation marks, commas and speech marks.

Handwriting at Year 4

We will continue the practice of joins developed in Years 2 and 3:

...slope joins to letters without ascenders: *an en in do um*

...bridge joins to letters without ascenders: *on ri vo wa fi*

...slope joins to letters with ascenders: *al eb it mb uh*

...bridge joins to letters with ascenders: *oh wh rl ot*

We will introduce joining from the following letters: *b g j p q s x y z*

... incorporating new forms of letters f and x:

... and resulting in a system of total joining:

fix six bags expert jelly quays zoo

Capital letters will remain unjoined.

Pupils will use joined writing for all writing, except for special projects or other aspects of presentation where different styles are required. For example, pupils may use printed script or capital letters for titles, headings, posters, etc.

We will teach the use of apostrophes to show possession and contraction and will show the pupils how to write apostrophes of appropriate shape, size and angle to fit well with their handwriting. We will revise the formation and use of punctuation marks, including commas, speech marks, question marks and exclamation marks.

We will encourage pupils to develop skills of writing quickly but legibly for notes and informal work. We will help pupils to realise that there are times when neat work is essential and other times when less formal writing is needed.

We will use 8mm lined paper or plain paper with an 8mm line guide, encouraging children to write letters of consistent size, where most letters sit on the line and descenders pass through it. We will show how to leave an appropriate gap between words, of approximately the width of two letters.

Handwriting at Years 5 and 6

We will continue the practice of joins developed in Year 4:

...slope joins to letters without ascenders: *an en in do um*

...bridge joins to letters without ascenders: *on ri vo wa fi*

...slope joins to letters with ascenders: *al eb it mb uh*

...bridge joins to letters with ascenders: *oh wh rl ot*

...including joins from the following letters: *b g j p q s x y z*

... incorporating these forms of letters f and x: *f x*

... and resulting in a system of total joining:

fix six bags expert jelly quays zoo

Capital letters will remain unjoined.

Pupils will use joined writing for all writing, except for special projects or other aspects of presentation where different styles are required. For example, pupils may use printed script or capital letters for titles, headings, posters, etc.

We will revise the use of apostrophes to show possession and contraction and will remind the pupils how to write apostrophes of appropriate shape, size and angle to fit well with their handwriting. We will consider the formation and use of punctuation marks, including commas, speech marks, question marks, exclamation marks, colons, semi-colons, dashes and brackets. We will check that pupils can write numerals neatly and correctly, as learnt in previous years. We will ensure that pupils can write pound signs correctly:

1 2 3 4 5 6 7 8 9 0 £

We will encourage pupils to develop skills of writing quickly but legibly for notes and informal work. We will help pupils to realise that there are times when neat work is essential and other times when less formal writing is needed.

Individual Lower Case Letters at Key Stage 2:

a b c d e f f

g g h i j j

k l m n o p

q r s t u v w

x x y y z

Numerals, pound signs and question marks:

1 2 3 4 5 6 7 8 9 0

£ ?

Formation of Capital Letters

Special Requirements for Left-Handed People:

Left-handed people can experience greater difficulties than right-handed people with writing. However, with appropriate guidance, left-handed children can develop handwriting which is just as neat as that of their right-handed classmates.

The following advice should be given to left-handed children:

Take care not to press too hard when you are writing.

Try to use a pen with ink which flows easily.

Left-handed people have to 'push' the pen across the paper rather than 'pull' it as right-handed people do.
Free-flowing ink reduces the need to press hard, thus avoiding digging into the paper.

Hold your paper at an angle so that you can see what you have written.

Left-handed people often find that their hand covers their writing so that they cannot see what they have written.
It is thought that this can inhibit correct spelling.
Covering the writing with the hand can also cause smudging.

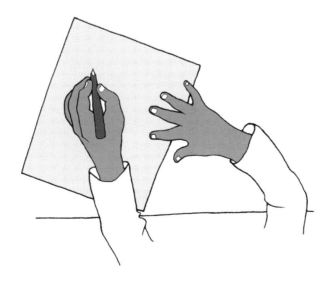

Here are some important rules
for best handwriting:

✓ Sit comfortably at your table, so
that you can see each letter as you
write.

✓ Hold your paper still.

✓ Make sure that your table is tidy.
You need plenty of space to work.

✓ Hold your pencil like this

if you are
right-handed ...

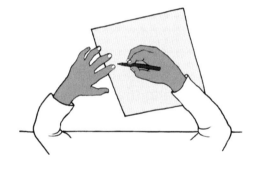

... and like this
if you are
left-handed.

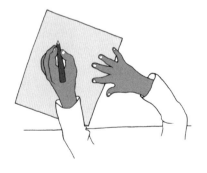

Always start your writing on this side of the page.

Go over my lines.

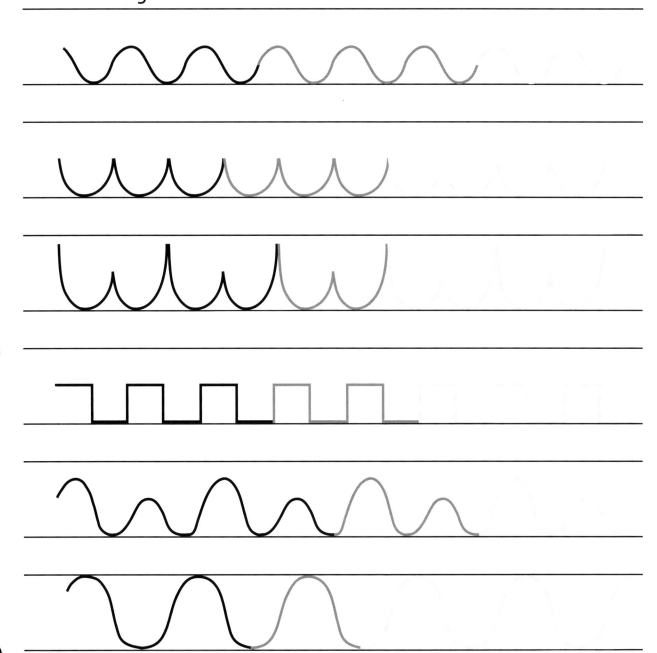

Go over these shapes.
Start each one where you see the pencil.

Begin each line
this side.

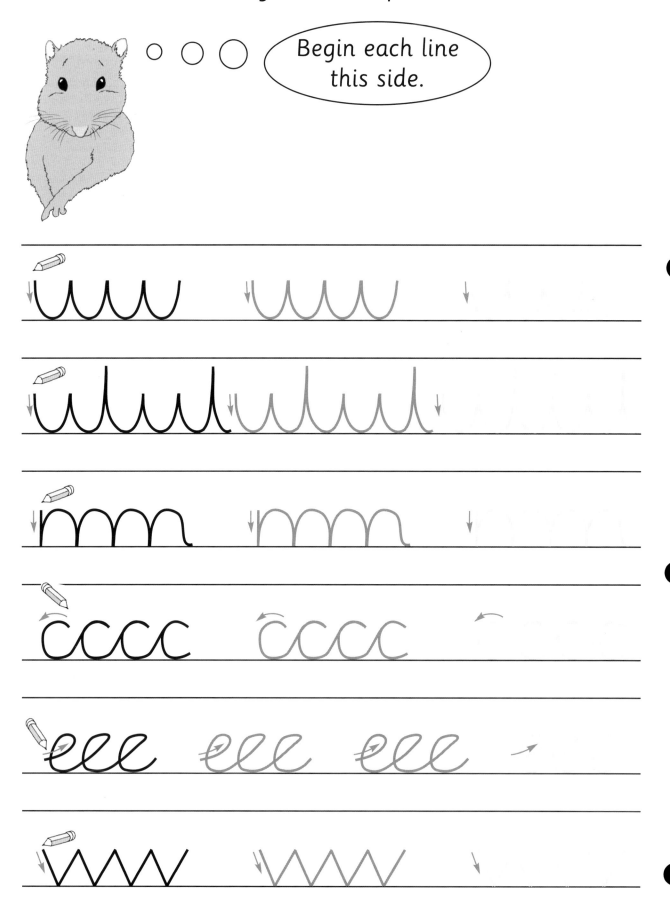

Go over this letter with your finger.

a

Use a pencil for the letters.

a a a a a a a a a

Using a coloured pencil, go over the letters to complete the picture.

apron

Go over this letter with your finger.

b

b b b b b b b b b

Use coloured pencils for these letters.

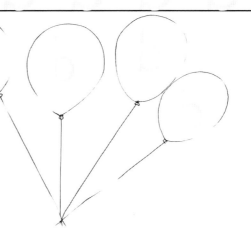

balloons

Go over the big letters with your finger.

C

Go over the small letters with a pencil.

c c c c c c c c c c

Use coloured pencils.

car

- -

d

Use a pencil to go over the small letters.

d d d d d d d d d

Use coloured pencils.

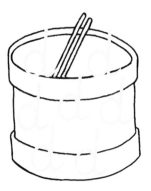

drum

Use your finger.

e

Use a pencil.

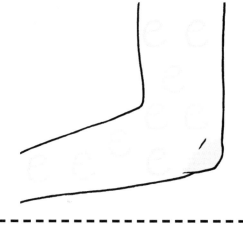

e e e e e e e e e

Use a coloured pencil.

elbow

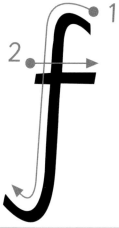

Use your finger.

2 *f* 1

Use a pencil.

f f f f f f

Use coloured pencils.

fish

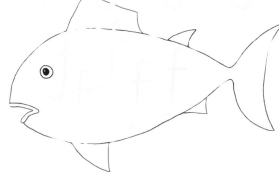

Use your finger.

Use a pencil.

g g g g g

Use coloured pencils.

gorilla

Use your finger to go over this big letter.

h

Use a pencil.

h h h h h

Use coloured pencils.

hand

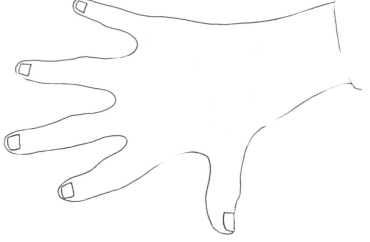

Use your finger.

1 2

Make the letter then put the dot on.

Now use a pencil.

Use coloured pencils.

ice-cube

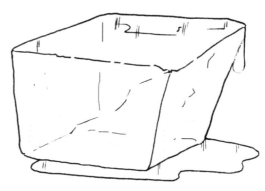

Use your finger.

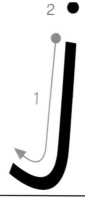

2

1

Make the letter then put the dot on.

Use a pencil.

Use coloured pencils.

jacket

Use your finger.

Use a pencil.

k k k k k

Use coloured pencils for the picture.

kettle

Use your finger.

Use a pencil.

l l l l l

Use coloured pencils for the picture.

lamp

Use a pencil.

m m m m m m m m

Use coloured pencils for the picture.

marbles

Use your finger.

Use a pencil.

n n n n n n n n

Use a coloured pencil.

nailbrush

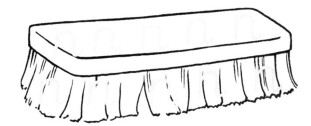

Use your finger.

Use a pencil.

o o o o o

Use coloured pencils.

octopus

Use your finger.

Use a pencil.

p p p p p

Use a coloured pencil.

parcel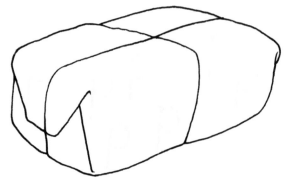

Go over this with your finger.

Use a pencil.

q q q q q q q q q

Use coloured pencils.

quilt

Use your finger to go over this letter.

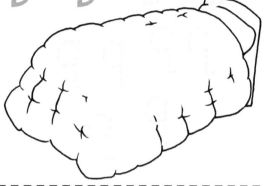

Use a pencil.

r r r r r r

Use coloured pencils.

rat

◯ ◯ ◯

Use a pencil.

Use coloured pencils.

stamp

- -

Use a finger. ◯ ◯ ◯

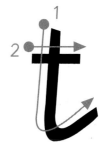

Put the cross on the t after
you have made the letter.

Use a pencil.

Use coloured pencils.

turtle

Use your finger.

Use a pencil.

u u u u u u

Use coloured pencils.

unicorn

Use a finger.

Use a pencil.

V v v v v v

Use coloured pencils.

volcano

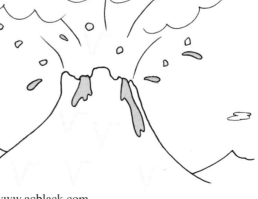

Use a pencil.

Use coloured pencils.

wallaby

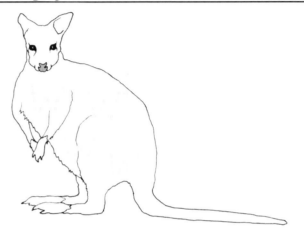

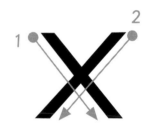

Use a pencil.

Use coloured pencils.

x-ray

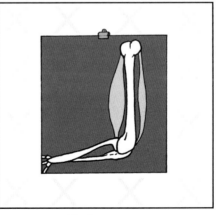

Use your finger. ○ ○ ○

Use a pencil.

ÿ y y y y

Use a coloured pencil.

yacht

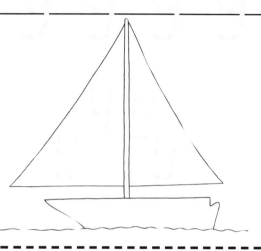

- -

Use your finger. ○ ○ ○

Use a pencil.

z z z z z

Use coloured pencils.

zebra

These words are important for you to read and write.

Go over mine and do some more on each line.

Make each letter with care.

can can can

come come

mum mum mum

to to to to to

✳ Read ✳ Go over ✳ Copy

mum can come to school

m

Now colour the picture.

© Andrew Brodie Publications www.acblack.com

Go over these words and do more on each line.

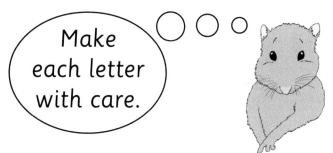

Make each letter with care.

at *at* *at*

cat *cat*

look *look*

my *my*

✳ Read ✳ Go over ✳ Copy

look at my cat

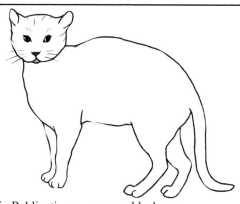

Now colour the picture.

Write I.

I I I I I ↓ ↓ ↓

Read and write.

going going

like like

on on

✳ Read   ✳ Go over   ✳ Copy

I like going on

holiday

© Andrew Brodie Publications   www.acblack.com

Go over my words and do some more on each line.

big big _____

● dog dog _____

play _____

the the _____

✳ Read ✳ Go over ✳ Copy

● the big dog _____

_____

can play _____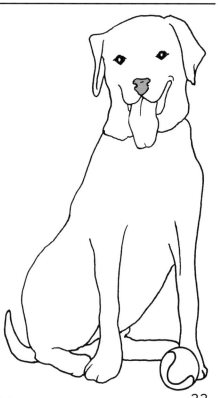

● Now colour the picture.

a a a a a

dad dad

up up up

went went

✳ Read ✳ Go over ✳ Copy

dad went

up a hill

Now colour the picture.

34 © Andrew Brodie Publications www.acblack.com

●

Go over the words and do some more. ○ ○ ○

and and

go go

we we

✳ Read
✳ Go over
✳ Copy

● **we can go**

and play

Now colour the picture.

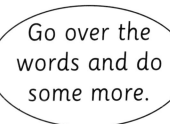

Go over the words and do some more.

for for

he he

is is

me me

✳ Read   ✳ Go over   ✳ Copy

he is looking

for me

Now colour the picture.

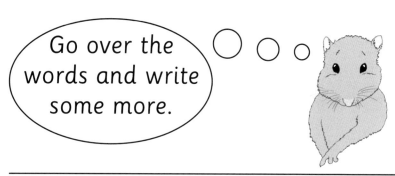

- Go over the words and write some more.

all *all*

- day

it *it*

was

❋ Read ❋ Go over ❋ Copy

- it was sunny all day

- Now colour the picture.

Go over the words and write some more.

away

get

said

she

✳ Read   ✳ Go over   ✳ Copy

get away from the bear

Now colour the picture.

Go over the words and write some more.

are are are

in in in

they they

* Read
* Go over
* Copy

they are in a box

Now colour the picture.

Go over the words and write some more.

of of _____

see see _____

you you _____

* Read   * Go over   * Copy

you see lots of flowers

Now colour the picture.

✳ Write the words.
✳ Read and copy the writing.
✳ Colour the pictures.

no

no I won't play

am

I am in a boat

this

this is a tree

yes

yes I like jelly

1

2

3

4

5

✳ Go over the writing. ✳ Copy the writing.
✳ Colour the picture.

1 tree

2 nests

3 flowers

4 birds

5 branches

Go over each number with care.

Then try some more on each line.

6 6

7 7

8 8

9 9

0 0

1 2 3 4 5

Once I caught a fish alive.

6 7 8 9 10

Then I let it go again.

A capital letter is used to begin a sentence.

Capital letters are used at the beginning of names and some important words.

✳ Copy the letters and complete each line.
✳ Make each letter with great care.

Aa Aa

Bb Bb

Cc Cc

Dd Dd

After tea it is

_____

time for bed.

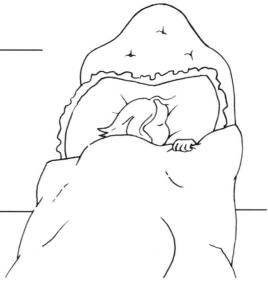

Copy the letters and complete each line.

Take care.

E e   E e
F f   F f
G g   G g
H h   H h

Girls and boys should

go to school.

SCHO

Copy the letters and complete each line.

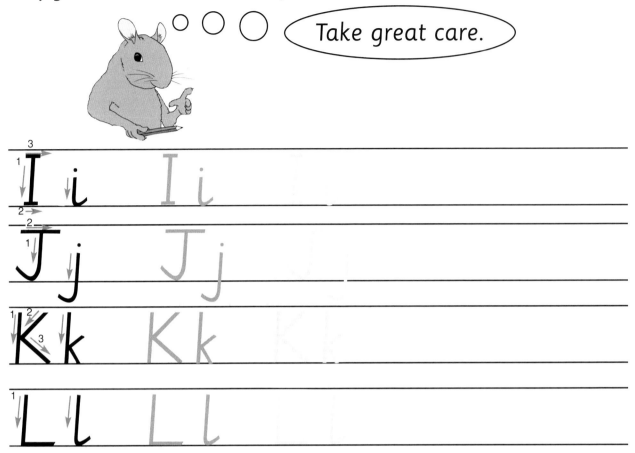

Take great care.

I i   I i

J j   J j

K k   K k

L l   L l

Little people can't push over trees.

Copy the letters and finish each line.

Make
each letter
carefully.

Mm   Mm

Nn   Nn

Oo   Oo

Pp   Pp

Old people must have some help.

Copy the letters and complete each line.

Hold your pencil correctly.

Make each letter with care.

Qq   Qq

Rr   Rr

Ss   Ss

Tt   Tt

✳ Read ✳ Go over ✳ Copy ✳ Complete the picture.

Three sisters saw their brother.

Uu Uu

Vv Vv

Ww Ww

Xx Xx

Yy Yy

Zz Zz

Who is in

_____

the house?

ou

All these words have ou in them.

our our

out out

about

house

would

could

He went out

of the house.

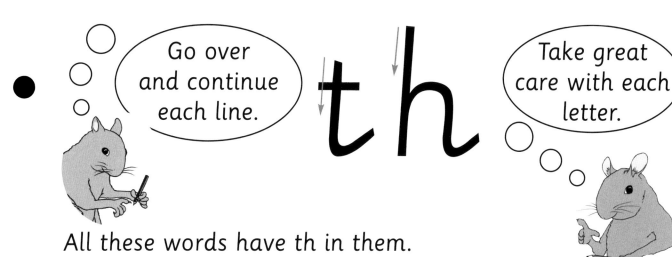

Go over and continue each line.

th

Take great care with each letter.

All these words have th in them.

them

then

there

these

with

another

three

_____

S

The letter s can be a bit troublesome.

Many people make it too big in their writing.

All these words have s in them.
Remember that s is a small letter.

as as as

has has has

last last last

so so so

us us us

seen seen

square

_____

m n

The little tail
at the end is to help
you when you learn to
join the letters.

man man

name

many

now

more

from

numbers _____

j y p

The dot goes on the j after the main part of the letter.

Go over the words and complete the lines.

jump   jump   jump

just   just   just

your   your

very   very   very

pull   pull

put   put

* Read   * Go over
* Copy   * Complete the picture.

parrots

_____

The letter r must always start at the top.

All these words have an r in them.
Go over and complete each line.

or or or or

ran ran ran

her her her her

here here

first first

were were

* Read * Go over * Copy * Complete the picture.

raindrops

_____

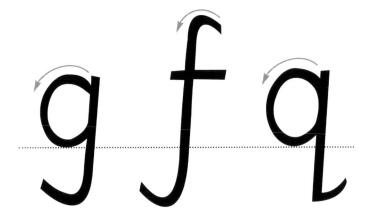

These letters have tails that hang under the line.

Go over the words and complete each line.

got   got

dig   dig

if   if if

off   off

square

quick   quick

gift

Go over the words and complete each line.

Monday _____

Tuesday _____

Wednesday _____

Thursday _____

Friday _____

Saturday _____

Sunday _____

There are 52 _____ weeks in a year.

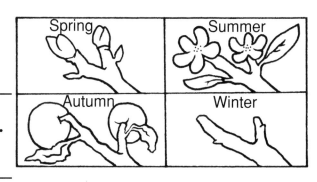

Go over the words and complete each line.

red red red red

blue blue blue

white white

black black

brown brown

yellow yellow

green green

✳ Read each word and colour each space correctly.

green [ ]   brown [ ]   blue [ ]
red [ ]
yellow [ ]   black [ ]   white [ ]

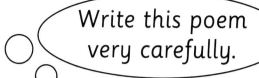

Check to see just how good your writing is.

Write this poem very carefully.

✳ Read
✳ Copy

On Monday I had cheese for dinner.

_____

On Tuesday I had eggs for tea.

_____

On Wednesday I played in the garden.

_____

On Thursday night I hurt my knee.

_____

On Friday I drank a glass of milk.

_____

On Saturday I went out to play.

_____

On Sunday I learned to ride my bike.

_____

It was Monday again the very next day.

_____

Joining your letters may seem slow at first.

After a while it will seem quick and easy.

Carefully join these pairs of letters.
Go over the letters and complete each line.

ee

ee ee ee ee

ea

ea ea ea ea

ai

ai ai ai ai

ue

ue ue ue ue

Fill the train with the letters.

Here are some more pairs of letters to join.

These pairs of letters are short words.

in

Put the dot on the i _after_ the n has been finished.

in in in in

to

Cross the t _after_ you have finished the o.

to to to to

do

do do do do

he

he he he he

no

no no no no

Whenever you are writing remember to...

...join the pairs of letters you have learned.

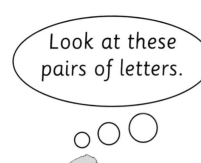

Look at these pairs of letters.

Some of them make short words.

ar

ar ar ar ar

am

am am am am

ay

ay ay ay ay

an

an an an an

When you do as remember to keep the s the same height as the a.

as

as as as as

er

er er er er er er

en

en en en en en en

em

em em em em em em

ew

ew ew ew ew ew ew

eg

eg eg eg eg

es

es es es es

mi

mi mi mi mi

my

my my my my

im

im im im im

is

is is is is

ic

ic ic ic ic

ip

ip ip ip ip

Join these letters
with care.

Remember to
keep s small.

us

us us us us

Dot the i
at the end.

ui

ui ui ui ui

um

um um um um

un

un un un un

ur

ur ur ur ur

up

up up up up

ab

ab

af

af af af af

ah

ah ah ah ah

ak

ak ak ak ak

al

al al al al

at

Only cross the t after writing the letters.

at at at at

it

it it it it it it it

if

if if if if if if

ik

ik ik ik ik ik ik

eh

eh eh eh eh eh

el

el el el el

eb

eb eb eb eb

Join these letters carefully.

ut

ut ut ut ut

ul

ul ul ul ul

ub

ub ub ub ub

cl

cl cl cl cl

ct

ct ct ct ct

Write over the letters
to fill the chimney.

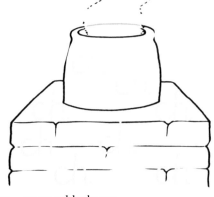

ht

ht ht ht ht

tt tt tt tt

lt lt lt lt

ll ll ll ll

mb mb mb mb

Go over the letters and write some more to fill the tent.

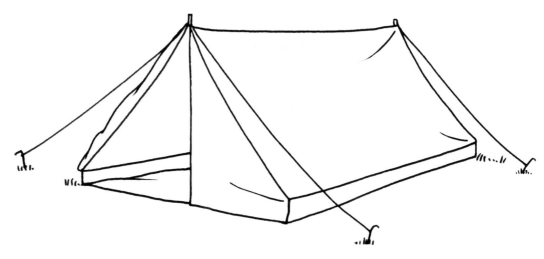

The first letters finish at the top so the join comes from there.

These are called bridge joins.

oa

oa oa oa oa

oo

oo oo oo oo

ou

ou ou ou ou

or

or or or or

on

on on on on

Write oi in the coins.

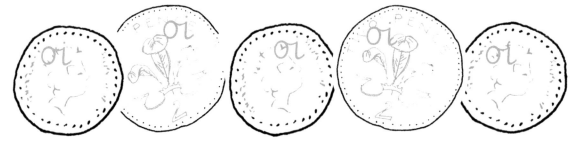

© Andrew Brodie Publications   www.acblack.com

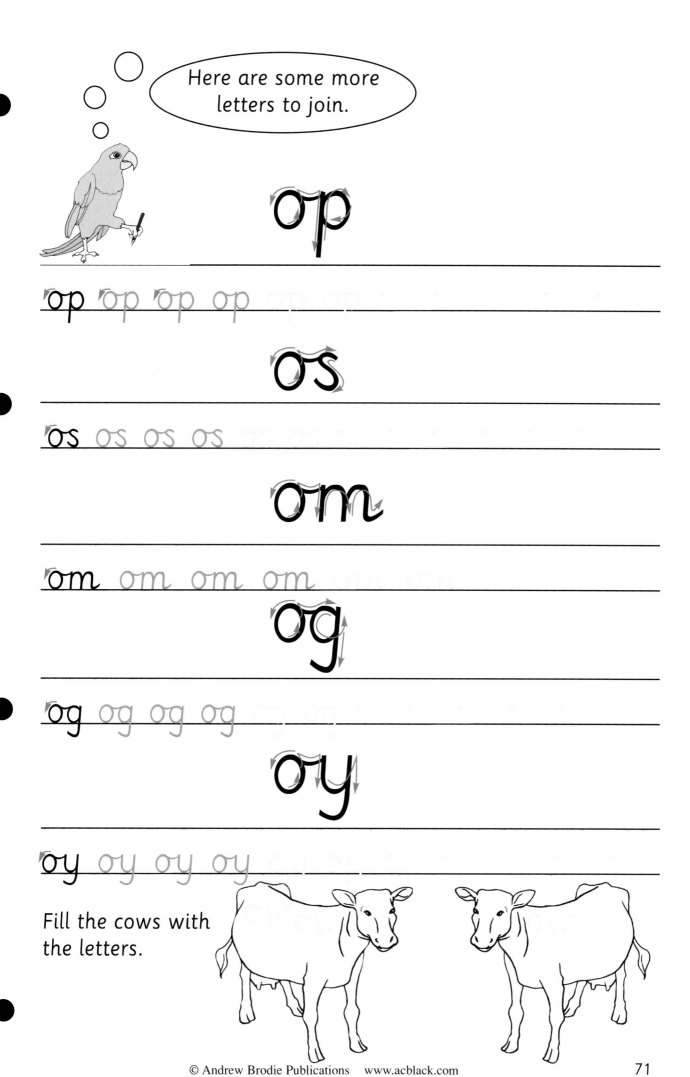

Here are some more
letters to join.

op

op op op op op op

os

os os os os os os

om

om om om om om om

og

og og og og og og

oy

oy oy oy oy

Fill the cows with
the letters.

Join the letters with care.

ra

ra ra ra ra

ru

ru ru ru ru

re

re re re re

ri

ri ri ri ri

rs

rs rs rs rs

ro

Go over the letters
and write some
more on the rocks.

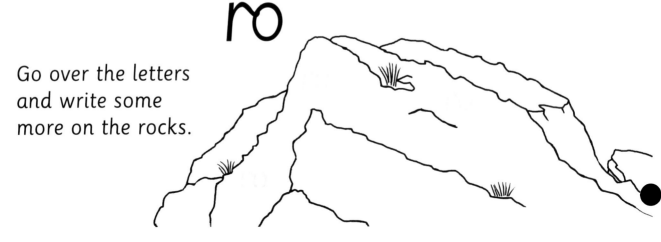

Here are some
more bridge joins.

va

va va va va

vi

Dot the i after you have
made both letters.

vi vi vi vi

wr

wr wr wr wr

wi

wi wi wi wi

wo

wo wo wo wo

Use the letters wa
to fill the water.

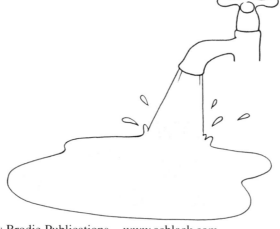

The letter f is joined to others from the line across it.

fi fi fi fi fi fi

fr fr fr fr fr fr

fo fo fo fo fo fo

fa fa fa fa fa fa

Go over the letters on the fence and write some more to fill it.

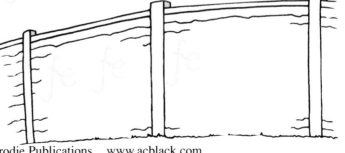

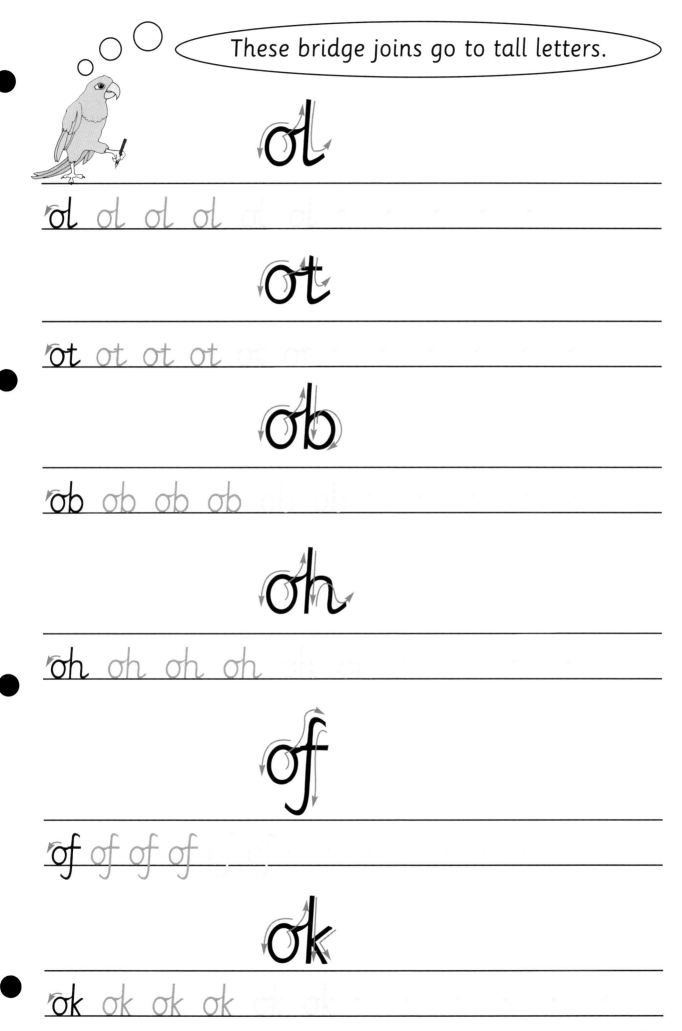

These bridge joins go to tall letters.

ol

ol ol ol ol

ot

ot ot ot ot

ob

ob ob ob ob

oh

oh oh oh oh

of

of of of of

ok

ok ok ok ok

Here are more pairs of letters to join with care.

rt

rt rt rt rt

rh

rh rh rh rh

rl

rl rl rl rl

rb

rb rb rb rb

rf

rf rf rf rf

Go over the letters
and write some more
to fill the shark.

Now let us try some whole words.

Do not take your pencil off the paper unless you have to.

duck

duck duck

hen

hen hen

chick

chick chick

Complete the pictures.

cup

cup cup cup cup

fork

fork fork fork fork

mug

mug mug mug mug

tea

tea tea tea tea tea tea

Write the words with care.

Use coloured pencils to complete the pictures.

hat _hat hat hat hat hat_

hair _hair hair hair hair_

face _face face face face_

neck _neck neck neck neck_

Here are parts of a word in a picture.

At the bottom is the whole name to write.

Use coloured pencils to complete the picture.

Now write the whole word.
Names begin with a capital letter.
Do <u>not</u> join the capital to the other letters.

Cinderella *Cinderella*

Continue each line of words.

Complete the picture.

fog fog

dog dog

log log

chip chip

chin chin

chain chain

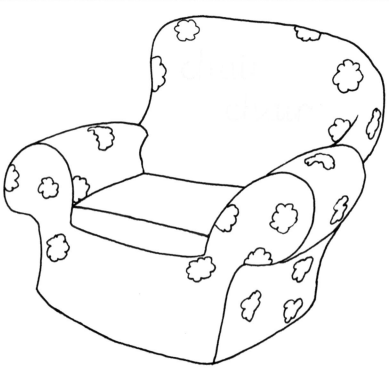

Continue each line of words.

Complete the picture.

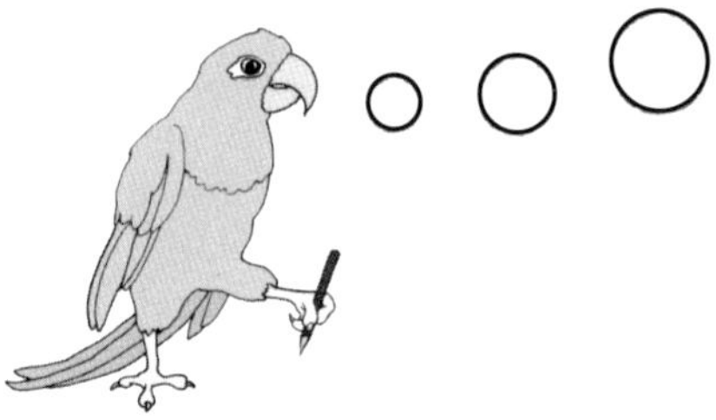

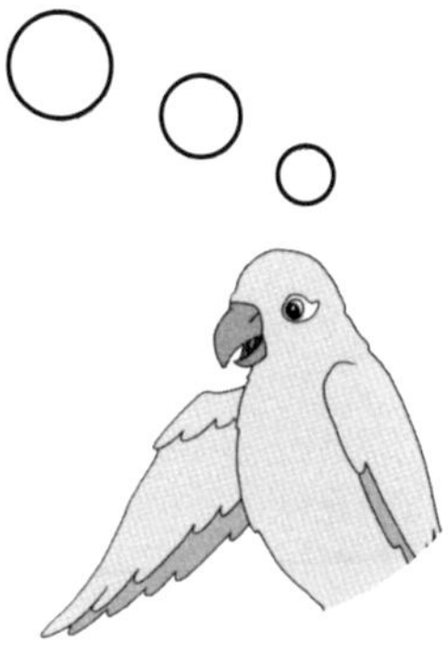

work work

floor floor

more more

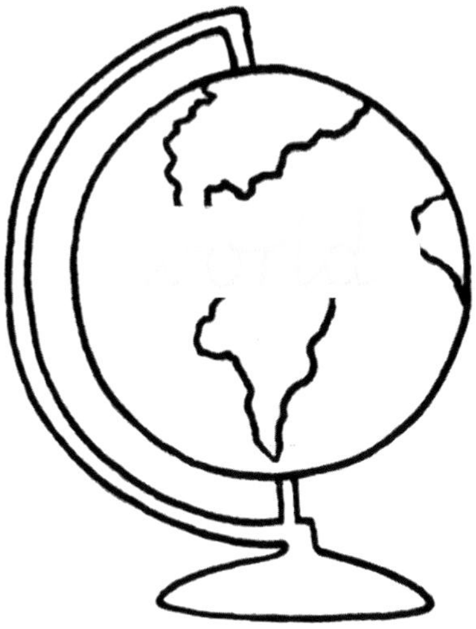

clean clean

team team

meat meat

dream dream

See how well you can write.

Remember not to join capital letters to the rest of the word.

☆ Do not join from b g j k p q s x y z, as you have not been taught how to yet.

☆ Copy this poem with care.

Alien Babies

Monday's child is green and red;

___

Tuesday's child has a very square head;

___

Wednesday's child is jagged and tall;

___

Thursday's child is shaped like a ball;

___

Friday's child looks like a snail;

___

Saturday's child has a very long tail;

___

And the child that is born on the seventh night,

___

Gives all the others a most terrible fright!

___